YOU KNOW YOU'RE

50

WHEN...

The Quiz of Your Lifetime

Mike Haskins

Illustrations by Ian Baker

summersdale

YOU KNOW YOU'RE 50 WHEN...

An Hachette UK Company
www.hachette.co.uk

Summersdale Publishers Ltd
Part of Octopus Publishing Group Limited
Carmelite House
50 Victoria Embankment
LONDON
EC4Y 0DZ
UK

www.summersdale.com

Printed and bound in Malta

ISBN: 978-1-78685-540-4

TO...

FROM...

INTRODUCTION

WOW! YOU'RE 50! CONGRATULATIONS!

You've lived 50 long years. That's 600 months! It's 2,600 weeks! 18,262 days! We could go on and work out the hours, minutes and seconds. But that might really begin to make you feel old.

But don't worry! Fifty is a fantastic age to be. You're not old.

Alright, you're not *that* old. You're still in your prime. Just about. You might have trouble arguing this point with a 20-year-old – but don't worry what those young whippersnappers say. OK, you may be a bit weathered by now, but hopefully most of you is still in serviceable condition. Look on yourself as the equivalent of a piece of shabby chic furniture.

And there's one thing that your 50 years on Earth have surely given you – experience! Just think of all the things that you've seen during your time. Think of the historical events that you've lived through. The innovations and inventions that you've seen introduced. The political and social upheaval you've witnessed. The achievements that have been made in your lifetime.

What do you mean, you can't remember any of them? That's the problem, isn't it? Life rushes by and there's so little time to dwell on all its riches and details. Then, when you look back, you find you can't remember much further than what you had for breakfast this morning.

So that's where this handy volume comes in. It's what you've been waiting for all these years. You've lived through 50 long years; now you can test yourself to see what you can remember about them.

And don't worry if the answers don't immediately come springing to mind. If you prefer, you can just turn the page after each quiz, look at the answers and revel in the nostalgic glow.

But let's get those 50-year-old synapses firing first and start the memories flooding back!

YOU KNOW YOU'RE 50 WHEN...

YOU WERE BROUGHT UP ON A DIET OF SWEETIES

Back in the 1970s and 1980s, when you were little (or reasonably little), no one had yet made the mistake of inventing healthy eating or dietary guidelines, so you may have lived on a diet of sweets, chocs and biscuits.

But can you fill in the missing words in the following advertising slogans and identify which products they were for?

Award yourself bonus points if you can remember exactly which of your teeth were wrecked by which of these sweets!

1 'Only the crumbliest,
flakiest chocolate
tastes like
....'

2 'They came in search of paradise, ...
....'

3 'Nuts! Who-ole hazelnuts! Uh!
....'

4 'A finger of
....'

5 'A glass and a half of full cream milk
.. ..'

6 'Do you love anyone enough to
....'

7 '.... ......! Made to make your mouth .....'

8 'Everybody knows that a .....
takes time a-chewin'

9 'Good, rich and thick –
. ...'

10 'The creamiest milk, the whitest bar,
... .'

YOU KNOW YOU'RE 50 WHEN...

YOU WERE BROUGHT UP ON A DIET OF SWEETIES

— ANSWERS —

1 'Only the crumbliest, flakiest chocolate tastes like chocolate never tasted before.'

This jingle was accompanied by a beautiful woman mesmerised by her Cadbury's Flake bar while canoeing through a waterfall or sitting in a state of undress on a sultry evening as a lizard tried to answer the phone for her.

2 'They came in search of paradise... and found it in Bounty.'

The Bounty ads featured gorgeous, scantily clad young people wading in and out of the sea on some tropical island. The reason given for their excursion was to enable them to sink their teeth into a coconut-filled chocolate bar. Couldn't they have just popped along to the newsagent's at home?

3 'Nuts! Who-ole hazelnuts! Uh! Cadbury's take 'em and they cover them in chocolate.'

The Whole Nut advert was sung to the tune of the 'Banana Boat Song' and there was something suggestive about the 'uh!' (accompanied by a pelvic thrust), not to mention the slightly suspect accent in which the jingle was sung!

4 'A finger of Fudge is just enough to give your kids a treat.'

The accompanying film featured a small schoolboy being distracted from a game of conkers by his mum giving his little sister a fudge bar which was 'full of Cadbury goodness', a health claim it would surely be difficult to get away with today.

5 'A glass and a half of full cream milk in every half pound.'

This may well have been true of a Dairy Milk chocolate bar, but then again no one ever told us exactly how big the glass was. It could have been a really tiny one!

6 'Do you love anyone enough to give them your last Rolo?'

For greater love hath no man than this – to give someone a small, chewy, toffee-filled sweet, even when it's the last one in the pack.

7 'Opal Fruits! Made to make your mouth water!'

Opal Fruits have been known as Starburst since 1998. Back in the 1970s, you probably thought a handful of Opal Fruits constituted your five-a-day.

8 'Everybody knows that a Texan takes time a-chewin''

Unusually for children's TV, these animated ads featured a slow-talking Clint Eastwood-like cowboy about to be executed by a firing squad or burnt at the stake. He only escaped thanks to the inordinate amount of time it took him to chew his Texan bar.

9 'Good, rich and thick – a milk chocolate brick.'

Yorkie was a chunky, manly chocolate bar, advertised with a long-distance truck driver whose one high spot of the day was eating his Yorkie bar. After all, who doesn't love chewing on a brick?

10 'The creamiest milk, the whitest bar, the goodness that's in Milky Bar.'

Another long-running, cowboy-themed advertising campaign involved the Milky Bar Kid, a character who resembled a miniature Alan Bennett in a cowboy outfit and who was apparently the prepubescent sheriff of a Wild West town, where he laid down the law by means of white chocolate.

YOU KNOW YOU'RE 50 WHEN...

YOU YEARN FOR THE TOYS AND GAMES OF THE 1970s

When you were a small child, you eagerly anticipated birthdays and Christmases to see if you would be given that latest, must-have game or toy on which you had set your little heart. Sadly, the most-desired playthings of your childhood have probably been lost in the mists of time – at least until you manage to buy them all over again at exorbitant prices on eBay. But how much do you remember about those toys and games?

1. Action Man had been launched in the 1960s, but which 1970s innovations assisted his ability to fire a gun and improve his vision?

2. Which gurning, orange, rubber, bouncy, inflatable toy of the 1970s was called Pon-Pon when originally launched in Italy?

3. The Rubik's Cube was launched in 1974. Which six colours were traditionally used on the cube?

4. What was the name of the dragster-inspired bike launched by Raleigh in the 1970s?

5. Which early-1970s toy comprised two plastic balls on the end of a string?

6. 'Space Oddity' was David Bowie's first hit in 1969 and was re-released in 1975 to become his first number one. But which toy electronic keyboard did the Thin White Duke use to play a solo on the track?

7   Which 1970s toys wobbled 'but didn't fall down'?

8   The American artist born Denise Holly Ulinskas was responsible for one of the most popular girls' dolls of the 1970s. Can you work out what her married name was?

9   Which game, launched in 1978, involved a competition between four different-coloured, herbivorous, semi-aquatic, white-marble-eating animals?

10   Which code-breaking board game featured on its box lid what appeared to be a bearded master criminal and his female Asian henchwoman?

YOU KNOW YOU'RE 50 WHEN...

YOU YEARN FOR THE TOYS AND GAMES OF THE 1970s

— ANSWERS —

1 In the 1970s Action Man gained gripping hands and moving 'Eagle Eyes'. Exactly the sort of thing that got other people in trouble around the same time.

2 Pon-Pon was known as the space hopper in the UK or the hippity hop in the USA. Although hugely successful in the 1970s, it ultimately failed to catch on as a suitable means of transport to get to school or work.

3 White, red, blue, orange, green, and yellow. The Rubik's Cube had over 43 quintillion (that's 43 followed by 18 zeros to you and me) combinations. Some kids could solve it in less than 5 seconds, while some of us had to peel off all the coloured labels and stick them back on in the right order to pretend we'd conquered the cube!

4 It was, of course, the Raleigh Chopper bike with its long, high-back seat, handlebars you had to reach up to and a small wheel at the front and a bigger wheel at the rear – to help you tip and fall off the back with your flared trousers flapping over your head.

5 Clackers. While holding the string, you could make the balls clack together in fast motion above and below your hand. Acquiring this skill did not, however, help qualify you for any form of paid employment in later life.

6 The Stylophone by Dubreq featured a tiny keyboard played with a stylus. Bowie inserted some fresh batteries to use the device again on his *Heathen* album in 2002, and it also features on Kraftwerk's 1981 song 'Pocket Calculator'. We nevertheless await any major classical works composed specifically for the Stylophone.

7 The toys that wobbled but didn't fall down were Weebles – small, plastic egg-shaped figures.

Unfortunately, as a result of all the junk food sold during the 1970s, many of us ended up a similar shape to Weebles ourselves.

8 Ms Ulinskas's married name was Mrs Holly Hobbie. Presumably she did not decide to marry Mr Hobbie simply for his cute-sounding name, but would her dolls have been so popular if she had, for example, married a Mr Shufflebottom?

9 The white-marble-eating animal game was Hungry Hungry Hippos. The hippos were called Henry (orange), Homer (green), Harry (yellow) and, because the makers of the game couldn't think of any more names beginning with 'H', Lizzie (purple). Never feed real hippos white marbles, though, as they are not part of their natural diet.

10 The code-breaking board game was Mastermind. The bearded supervillain on the box presumably intended to take over Earth by strategic use of the blue, green, red, yellow, white and black plastic pegs.

YOU KNOW YOU'RE 50 WHEN...

YOU CAN JUST ABOUT REMEMBER WHAT HAPPENED IN THE POLITICS OF THE LATE 1970s AND EARLY 1980s

OK, obviously you were too young to vote back then and your main political grievance during the late 1970s and early 1980s was the fact that they moved kids programmes to BBC2 whenever the Budget was on. Nevertheless, do you recall the following murky political goings-on?

1. Which UK political party leader was tried for conspiracy to murder in 1979?

2. In 1991 about whom or what did Margaret Thatcher remark: 'Every prime minister needs a Willie!'

3. Which Shakespearian phrase from Richard III became associated with the end of 1978 and beginning of 1979?

4. Liverpool Council had to store corpses in a factory in Speke as a result of a strike by which group of workers?

5. Which political group did Prime Minister James Callaghan describe as being like 'turkeys voting for Christmas'?

6. The Social Democratic Party was founded on 26 March 1981 by four ex-Labour politicians. How many of them can you name?

7   What nickname was given to Mrs Thatcher in 1976 by the *Soviet Army Journal* and was later the title of the film about her life starring Meryl Streep?

8   In 1975, writer and broadcaster Clive James described Thatcher's voice as sounding like something going down a blackboard. What was it?

9   A 1979 Conservative election poster showed a long queue of people queuing for unemployment benefit. What was the slogan that appeared on the poster? And, if you're feeling particularly bright, which advertising company was responsible for it?

10 Which Labour leader was berated by the press for wearing a donkey jacket at the Cenotaph in November 1981?

YOU KNOW YOU'RE 50 WHEN...

YOU CAN JUST ABOUT REMEMBER WHAT HAPPENED IN THE POLITICS OF THE LATE 1970s AND EARLY 1980s

— ANSWERS —

1. Jeremy Thorpe, leader of the Liberal Party. In those days the Liberals had sex scandals, guilty secrets and murder plots. Rather than being a political party, the Liberals of the 1970s could have been turned into a racy TV drama. And indeed in 2018 they were!

2. No, Mrs Thatcher was not referring to some contraption purchased from the Ann Summers shop, but to Willie Whitelaw, her

first Home Secretary and Deputy Leader of the Conservative Party. She didn't even realise her double entendre. Who says politicians are out of touch with the people?

3 The 'winter of discontent' – not only was it filled with discontent as a result of widespread strikes by trade unions, the winter of 1978/79 was a particularly chilly and snowy one as well.

4 It was because of a 14-day strike by gravediggers who were members of the General and Municipal Workers Union in Liverpool and Tameside.

5 Callaghan was talking about the Scottish Nationalists who backed a motion of no confidence in his Labour government. The motion was carried by 311 votes to 310 and ushered in 18 years of Conservative rule, first under Margaret Thatcher and then under John Major.

6 The founders of the SDP were Roy Jenkins, Shirley Williams, David Owen and Bill Rodgers. It was a bit like a political supergroup (if you can imagine a supergroup led by a small, round, bespectacled Welshman).

7 She was called The Iron Lady. Please note, this did not mean that Mrs T was in any way related to Robert Downey Jr.

8 Clive James described Mrs Thatcher's voice as sounding like a cat going down a blackboard. She managed to improve her tone considerably in later years, becoming deeper and less shrill – like a cat going down a blackboard but slightly more slowly.

9 The slogan 'Labour Isn't Working' was dreamt up by advertising company Saatchi and Saatchi. At the time of Mrs Thatcher's election in 1979, the unemployment rate was between 5 and 6 per cent. When she left office in 1990, it was more or less the same, but for some reason the Saatchis didn't create a poster about that.

10 Michael Foot, the great socialist writer and intellectual, had become a perhaps slightly less great leader of the Labour Party in 1980. The coat he wore was not in fact a donkey jacket, but an expensive overcoat selected by his wife. Unfortunately, when he put it on it suddenly seemed to look like something out of a charity bin.

YOU KNOW YOU'RE 50 WHEN...

YOU REMEMBER SEEING THESE FILMS AT CHILD ADMISSION PRICES

When you were little, you and your family could enjoy a trip to the pictures for a fraction of the price of a bucket of popcorn today. Once there, you experienced visions of extraordinary wonder – or at least you would have if you had been able to see anything through the cigarette fumes drifting across the screen from the seats reserved for patrons who wished to smoke.

But did you manage to see enough to remember the following films of your youth?

1. What type of weaponry was predominantly used in a 1976 prohibition-era gangster movie starring Scott Baio and Jodie Foster?

2. Who rode again in 1974, went to Monte Carlo in 1977 and finally went bananas in 1980?

3. Which ocean-set movie became the highest grossing in film history after its release in 1975? And which 1977 space adventure then took the crown?

4. Which 1978 superhero film featured Marlon Brando, Gene Hackman, Trevor Howard and Terence Stamp?

5. Who was afraid, alone and three million light years from home in 1982?

6. Which 1981 film begins with the hero travelling into a Peruvian temple, taking a golden idol and finding himself pursued by an enormous boulder?

7　Who was here to save the world in 1984 (and to save New York from the Stay Puft Marshmallow Man)?

8　Also in 1984, which creatures were you warned not to get wet, to keep out of bright light and never to feed after midnight?

9　Which 1984 horror classic marked Johnny Depp's big-screen debut?

10　In 1985, who was the only kid ever to get into trouble before he was born?

YOU KNOW YOU'RE 50 WHEN...

YOU REMEMBER SEEING THESE FILMS AT CHILD ADMISSION PRICES

— ANSWERS —

1 The film was *Bugsy Malone* and the weapons used were splurge guns. If only real-world conflicts could be settled by means of splurge guns!

2 It was Herbie, the VW Beetle with a mind of its own first seen in Disney's 1968 film *The Love Bug*. Back in your youth, a car that could think for itself seemed a crazy idea, but soon we'll all be in self-driving cars that have minds of their own!

3 Steven Spielberg's *Jaws* became the highest-grossing movie of all time after its release in 1975, then in 1977 George Lucas' *Star Wars* took the record.

4 *Superman*, starring Christopher Reeve. Marlon Brando was said to have been paid $3.7 million for his two weeks' work on the film. This still wasn't enough to get Brando to learn his lines, though, which had to be printed for him on the nappy worn by the infant Superman!

5 It was, of course, E.T., who, in the film *E.T. the Extra Terrestrial*, had to phone home across the universe. It's probably best not to think what the roaming charges might have been!

6 *Raiders of the Lost Ark* – exactly how often did Professor Indiana Jones have to use his bullwhip to bring order when he was teaching his archaeology lessons?

7 *Ghostbusters*, the story of a group of parapsychologists who set up a business that they clearly designed to be to paranormal manifestations what Dyno-Rod is to blocked drains!

8 Gremlins were the creatures in the film about getting a cute, furry little creature as a pet but finding out it goes on to cause mayhem and destruction. If you want to find out what that's like in real life, try getting yourself a Jack Russell.

9 *A Nightmare on Elm Street*, featuring Freddy Krueger, a villain with a hand of lethally sharp metal blades, which presumably made going to the toilet a nightmare in itself.

10 In *Back to the Future*, Michael J. Fox, as Marty McFly, went back to 1955 to invent rock and roll before anyone else had thought of it.

YOU KNOW YOU'RE 50 WHEN...

YOU REMEMBER WHEN TOBACCO AND FAGS WERE ADVERTISED ON TV

When you were a kid, grown-ups smoked everywhere around you at all times, so by the time you were old enough to smoke yourself, you were probably already hooked! So it should be no problem to answer the following.

1. What was the wording of the health warning printed on cigarette packets in the 1970s?

2. Happiness was said to be which sort of cigar?

3. Can you complete this slogan for a brand of cigarettes: 'Come to where the flavour is. ....'?

4. Who was alleged to be 'the patron saint of pipe smokers'?

5. Which brand of tinned tobacco had the slogan 'NONE NICER' on its lid?

6. Which cigarettes were advertised by a piece of purple fabric with a hole in it?

7. Which cigars offered 'sheer enjoyment'?

8. According to adverts for a certain pipe tobacco, nothing should disturb which moment?

9. Which brand of cigarettes and tobacco had a bearded sailor on the pack?

10. Which brand of tobacco offered you the chance 'to live in peace with your pipe'?

YOU KNOW YOU'RE 50 WHEN...

YOU REMEMBER WHEN TOBACCO AND FAGS WERE ADVERTISED ON TV

— ANSWERS —

1. WARNING by H.M. Government. SMOKING CAN DAMAGE YOUR HEALTH – 30 years later, it was changed to 'TOBACCO SERIOUSLY DAMAGES HEALTH', which sounded slightly less like the damage was optional!

2. Happiness was 'a cigar called Hamlet'. Even if you've never enjoyed a cigar in your life, the sounds of Bach's 'Air on a G String', which accompanied the TV adverts, may cause you to reminisce wistfully about smoking!

3 'Come to Marlboro Country!' Marlboro cigarettes were advertised with manly images of the 'Marlboro man' with his horses and cattle against a backdrop of rocky mountains. Sadly, four of the Marlboro men died from smoking-related diseases, so smoking was even more dangerous than living in the Wild West.

4 St Bruno – there have, in fact, been several real-life Saint Brunos, but they all lived hundreds of years before tobacco was brought back from the New World.

5 Three Nuns tobacco was punningly advertised with the slogan 'NONE NICER'. Did smoking offer some sort of religious serenity? Or was it just a fast way to get to heaven?

6 Silk Cut. As tobacco advertising was prevented from portraying status, coolness or sexual attractiveness, the Silk Cut people used abstract images featuring the colours of the packet. Many smokers couldn't see a torn piece of purple silk without becoming desperate for a fag.

7 Manikin cigars offered 'sheer enjoyment'. Their adverts featured very scantily clad young ladies splashing around in tropical streams and ponds, for no very obvious reason connected to the subject of cigars!

8 'Nothing should disturb that Condor moment.' The man in the TV adverts for Condor again seemed to experience some sort of blissful transcendence. Was it really only tobacco he was putting in his pipe?

9 Player's Navy Cut – the pack was adorned with a picture of a rough bearded type in a sailor hat and uniform. Players were therefore the people who really put the 'tar' in 'Jolly Jack Tar'.

10 Mellow Virginia from Benson and Hedges let you live in peace with your pipe. Perhaps if you puffed enough you'd disappear in a cloud of smoke and no one could see or bother you.

YOU KNOW YOU'RE 50 WHEN...

YOU CAN NEVER FORGET THE CHRISTMAS NUMBER ONES OF THE 1970s AND 1980s

In recent times the Christmas number one has often been a plodding sickly anthem belted out by the winner of a recent TV singing contest. Back in your childhood days, however, the Christmas number one was a hotly contested musical prize that would be won by a supreme combination of pop songwriting, musical craft and performance. Or was it?

1972: 'Long Haired Lover from Liverpool'

1. Which annoying child star sang it?

2. How old was he at the time this record was a hit?

3. How many of his siblings can you name?

4. Why do all of his family have such gleaming white teeth?

5. Osmondmania was supplanted by the appearance of which tartan-clad boy band?

1975: 'Bohemian Rhapsody'

1. Which group recorded this classic Christmas number one?

2. How many weeks did it spend in the top slot?

3. Which two words in the lyrics were also the title of the song which knocked it off number one?

4 Can you name the Italian scientist, the operatic character and the commedia dell'arte clown who are all mentioned in the song?

5 This band reached number one in the UK singles charts in their own right on three occasions, but can you remember the singles involved?

1980: 'There's No One Quite Like Grandma'

1 What was the name of the choir who sang this song?

2 From which northern town did they come from?

3 What was the name of the hit song about painter L. S. Lowry on which the choir had previously appeared?

4   The song was written in celebration of which member of the Royal Family?

5   What was the name of the then recently deceased singer who was knocked off number one by this record (and by whom it was subsequently knocked off the top spot two weeks later)?

1984: 'Do They Know It's Christmas?'

1   Which two music stars wrote this unforgettable charity song?

2   Who presented the BBC news reports about famine in East Africa that inspired the song?

3   Who sings the song's first line?

4   Which singer gets to sing their own name in the course of the song?

5   How many different official versions of 'Do They Know It's Christmas?' have been released?

YOU KNOW YOU'RE 50 WHEN...

YOU CAN NEVER FORGET THE CHRISTMAS NUMBER ONES OF THE 1970s AND 1980s

— ANSWERS —

Answers to 'Long Haired Lover from Liverpool'

1. The gurning chipmunk was little Jimmy Osmond.

2. Nine years old! He was born in April 1963 and hit the top spot at Christmas in 1972.

3. The Osmond Brothers band comprised Alan, Wayne, Merrill, Jay and, of course, heart-throb Donny. There was also Marie, the Osmond

sister, and two elder brothers, Virl and Tom, both born with severe hearing difficulties.

4 Supposedly they kept their teeth shiny because, as clean-living members of the Mormon church, they did not smoke or drink tea or coffee.

5 Scottish pop sensations, the Bay City Rollers, supplanted the Osmonds in many young hearts, reached number one with 'Bye Bye Baby' in 1975 and have lived on ever since in the form of various different line-ups and court cases.

Answers to 'Bohemian Rhapsody'

1 Queen – not to be confused with *the* Queen who gets her own message on TV every single Christmas, traditionally just after *Top of the Pops* is screened.

2 Nine weeks, and every week on *Top of the Pops* we had to watch the same video.

3 'Mamma Mia' is in the lyrics of 'Bohemian Rhapsody' and was also the title of the stonking ABBA hit that replaced it at number one.

4 Galileo, Figaro and Scaramouche.

5 Queen in their own right reached number one with 'Bohemian Rhapsody' in 1975; 'Innuendo' in 1991 and then again with the re-release of 'Bohemian Rhapsody' (backed with 'These Are the Days of Our Lives') in 1991 after Freddie Mercury's death. They also scored number ones with 'Under Pressure' (with David Bowie) in 1981; 'Somebody to Love' (with George Michael) in 1993; and 'We Will Rock You' (with 5ive) in 2000. 'We Are the Champions' only reached number two in 1977, so rendering its title slightly overoptimistic.

Answers to 'There's No One Quite Like Grandma'

1 St Winifred's School Choir – the choir of an actual Roman Catholic primary school. If the make-up of the choir was anything to go by, girls vastly outnumbered boys at this establishment.

2 Stockport in Greater Manchester. Musicians who have recorded their greatest work in Stockport include 10cc, Joy Division, The Stone Roses and... St Winifred's School Choir!

3 'Matchstalk Men and Matchstalk Cats and Dogs', a 1978 song about the painter L. S. Lowry by Brian and Michael, which also reached number one. St Winifred's School Choir have therefore been on two 'one-hit wonder' number one records!

4 The Queen Mum – God bless her! She had turned 80 the year the record was released and composer Gordon Lorenz said he wrote it with her in mind. That was all very nice for the Queen Mum, but we can only guess what Gordon Lorenz's actual grandmother might have thought about this.

5 John Lennon. The recently murdered Beatle had been at number one with 'Just Like Starting Over' and then replaced St Winifred's at number one with a re-release of 'Imagine'.

Answers to 'Do They Know It's Christmas?'

1 Midge Ure and Bob Geldof. Presumably Midge had to overrule Sir Bob's original idea to call the song 'Give Us Your ****ing Money!'

2 Michael Buerk presented a series of harrowing reports on the BBC News detailing the extent of that year's famine in Ethiopia.

3 Paul Young, the 'Wherever I Lay My Hat' hit maker. Perhaps the association between hats and charity collections got him the job!

4 Sting sings the lyrics 'the bitter sting of tears'. It's a good job all the other singers didn't insist on having their own names woven into the lyrics – 'Simon le Bon' would have involved quite a challenge.

5 There have been four Band Aid releases: the original version in 1984; Band Aid II in 1989 (with Kylie, Jason and friends); Band Aid 20 in 2004 (included Dido, Chris Martin and Robbie Williams); and 2014's Band Aid 30 (included Ed Sheeran, Rita Ora and Sam Smith). Bono has featured on three of the four versions, so maybe he's been locked in the studio since 1984.

YOU KNOW YOU'RE 50 WHEN...

YOU STILL LOVE LOOKING THROUGH THE BOOKS YOU READ AS A CHILD

Of course, when you were young, there was absolutely nothing to do. As a result, you frequently became so bored you had no choice but to settle down with a great book – instead of being able to while away the time looking up rubbish on the internet. But can you identify the following children's and teenage books that you might have read in the 1970s and 1980s?

1. The 1970 book in which farmers Boggis, Bunce and Bean are outsmarted.

2. A series that began with a 1970 book detailing the unlikely but affectionate relationship between two different breeds of amphibian.

3. An adventure story first published in 1972 that begins in Sandleford, Berkshire with one character having a premonition that his family's home is about to be destroyed.

4. A 1973 novel about a girl and her brother being evacuated to Wales in World War Two.

5. A 1975 novel following the relationship of Michael and Katherine, but which ends with Katherine getting a call from Theo.

6. First published in 1978, a picture book with no words that begins with a boy waking on a cold winter's morning.

7 A 1979 book in which Bastian Balthazar Bux steals an apparently magical book about the land of Fantasia.

8 A 1982 novel in which the hero lusts after Pandora Braithwaite while his mother and father pair off respectively with Mr 'Creep' Lucas and Doreen 'the Stick Insect' Slater.

9 A 1983 novel in which Rincewind has to ensure the safety of Twoflower in Ankh-Morpork to avoid invasion by the Agatean Empire.

10 A 1987 book in which the hero travels to a mall, a beach, a ski resort, a campsite, a beach, a railway station, an airport, a sports stadium, a museum, the sea, a safari park, a department shop and a fairground – and finds them all quite crowded.

YOU KNOW YOU'RE 50 WHEN...

YOU STILL LOVE LOOKING THROUGH THE BOOKS YOU READ AS A CHILD

— ANSWERS —

1 In Roald Dahl's novel, Boggis, Bunce and Bean are three mean and ugly farmers whose chickens, ducks and turkeys are stolen by *Fantastic Mr Fox*.

2 Arnold Lobel's picture book *Frog and Toad Are Friends* tells a series of stories in which Frog and Toad help each other out in various ways rarely seen in nature.

3 Fiver has a vision of the destruction of his and his fellow rabbits' warren at the beginning of Richard Adams' *Watership Down*, one of the greatest epic tales ever to be set in Berkshire!

4 *Carrie's War* by Nina Bawden tells the story of Carrie Willow, her brother Nick and their friend Albert Sandwich being evacuated to Wales.

5 Judy Blume's novel *Forever* is a sensitive presentation of teenage sexuality back in the days before social media came along and presented it all in a much less considerate way.

6 Raymond Briggs' *The Snowman* is the story of the friendship between a young boy and the snowman he builds – a relationship which is tragically doomed by the sun coming up the following day.

7 Bastian Balthazar Bux appears in Michael Ende's *The Neverending Story*, which, in contravention of the Trade Descriptions Act, in fact ends after 528 pages (spoiler alert!).

8 Sue Townsend's *The Secret Diary of Adrian Mole Aged 13 ¾* featured Pandora and the rest. It wasn't much of a secret in the end, though, as it sold more than 20 million copies!

9 Rincewind and Twoflower appear in *The Colour of Magic*, the first of Terry Pratchett's 41 Discworld novels, which together sold in excess of 85 million copies and allowed Terry to give up his job working at the Central Electricity Board.

10 Martin Handford's 1987 book *Where's Wally?* featured the eponymous character hidden in various crowded locations. In the USA and Canada, Wally was called Waldo. In France he was Charlie and in Germany he was Walter. What with all this hiding in crowds and going by various aliases, could Wally have been some sort of international criminal or spy?

YOU KNOW YOU'RE 50 WHEN...

YOUR DEFINITION OF STATE-OF-THE-ART TECHNOLOGY OR INNOVATIVE DEVELOPMENT IS 'STUFF FROM THE 1970s'

The unfortunate thing for 50-year-olds is that the exciting new inventions and innovations you gawped at on programmes such as *Tomorrow's World* are now 40 years old and regarded by young people as pitifully primitive. See if you remember these moments of technological triumph that happened during your early years.

1. In the history of shopping, what was significant about the purchase of a packet of Juicy Fruit chewing gum at 8.01 a.m. on 26 June 1974 in Marsh's Supermarket in Troy, Ohio?

2. What medical manoeuvre changed the life of speedy eaters in 1974?

3. Also in 1974, a weak adhesive developed some years earlier by Dr Spencer Silver finally found a use on which stationery product?

4. Which innovation in drink-can technology first appeared in 1975?

5. Three people founded the Apple computer company in April 1976. How many of them can you name?

6. How did Louise Brown make history on the day she was born – 25 July 1978?

7 The first VHS video recorder went on sale in 1978. But what did VHS stand for? And which alternative video recording system had been launched by Sony in 1975?

8 Philips marketed a third type of recorder, the Video 2000. What advantage did its marketing people claim for this system?

9 Sony introduced the Walkman in 1979. What was unusual about the first model's earphone sockets?

10 What did *Tomorrow's World* presenter Kieran Prendiville do to a CD in 1981 to show that it was tougher than vinyl?

YOU KNOW YOU'RE 50 WHEN...

YOUR DEFINITION OF STATE-OF-THE-ART TECHNOLOGY OR INNOVATIVE DEVELOPMENT IS 'STUFF FROM THE 1970s'

— ANSWERS —

1. It was the first time any product had been bought using a scanned barcode. Did it really scan on the first attempt or did the till assistant have to give up and type the number in?

2. In June 1974 the Heimlich manoeuvre was first described by Doctor Henry Heimlich. Heimlich also happened to be the uncle of Anson Williams,

who played 'Potsie' in the TV series *Happy Days*, which debuted the same year.

3 Post-it notes – other people had wanted to tell Dr Silver about this idea earlier, but they didn't have anything they could write it down on and then stick on his desk.

4 The push-in tab! Before that, the streets were littered with discarded can tabs. Afterwards, they were littered with entire discarded cans!

5 Steve Jobs, Steve Wozniak and Ronald Wayne (the latter doesn't get quite as much attention or films made about him as the first two!). The Apple Mark 1 cost $666.66 – surely the price tag of the beast!

6 Newspaper reports described Louise as the world's first 'test-tube baby'. Since her birth, the process that enabled her conception has become better known as IVF (in vitro fertilisation – not, as some believe, a reference to the world's second test-tube baby, Ivy Effe).

7 VHS stood for Video Home System. Sony had launched Betamax earlier and it was generally agreed that it provided better-quality recordings than VHS, but they still lost the ensuing battle of the formats.

8. You could turn Philips' tapes over and record for longer than either VHS or Betamax would allow. Another advantage that people couldn't be bothered with, and which therefore didn't catch on.

9. Originally, the Walkman had two earphone sockets, so you and a friend could both plug in your earphones together before shouting at each other whenever you needed to say anything.

10. He scratched it to demonstrate it would still play. Many people remember a different but now lost TV stunt, in which a presenter spread jam on a CD, presumably trying to wreck not just his CD but his CD player at the same time!

YOU KNOW YOU'RE 50 WHEN...

THE EVENTS OF THE 1980s SEEM LIKE YESTERDAY

Did you ever wear shoulder pads to school? Or did you have your hair in a tight perm? Or crafted into a mullet? Or even in a tight permed mullet? Did you ever hang round the local shopping centre dressed up like Boy George or Toyah? Those might all be aspects of the 1980s you'd rather forget, so can you instead recall the following truly significant events?

1. Who signed the most fateful autograph of his life on 8 December 1980?

2. What took off for the first time on 12 April 1981?

3. Who got married on Wednesday 29 July 1981?

4. Which 'war' lasted from 2 April until 14 June 1982?

5. A total of 24 musical groups or solo singers appeared on stage at Wembley for Live Aid on Saturday 13 July 1985. How many can you name?

6. Which adverts warned us all not to 'die of ignorance'?

7. What rare celestial event could be seen – just about – during February 1986?

8. Which city was evacuated at the end of April 1986?

YOU KNOW YOU'RE 50 WHEN...

THE EVENTS OF THE 1980s SEEM LIKE YESTERDAY

— ANSWERS —

1   John Lennon, who was murdered by Mark Chapman shortly before 11 p.m. on 8 December 1980 outside the ex-Beatle's home at the Dakota Building in New York City. Six hours earlier, Chapman had got him to autograph a copy of his latest album, *Double Fantasy*.

2   The Space Shuttle's maiden flight was on 12 April 1981 and involved orbiting Earth 37 times. The Space Shuttle was the world's first reusable spacecraft.

3 Prince Charles and Lady Diana Spencer were married at St Paul's Cathedral in London in July 1981. Over a billion TV viewers were said to have watched the ceremony. If, fifteen years later, they'd got to fight out their divorce head-to-head on live television, they might have got even better viewing figures!

4 In the spring of 1982, the UK and Argentina fought each other in the Falklands Conflict (it is often incorrectly referred to as the Falklands War, but war was never formally declared by either country).

5 The acts who appeared at Live Aid were: Status Quo; The Style Council; The Boomtown Rats; Adam Ant; Ultravox; Spandau Ballet; Elvis Costello; Nik Kershaw; Sade; Sting; Phil Collins; Howard Jones; Bryan Ferry; U2; Paul Young; Alison Moyet; Dire Straits; Queen; David Bowie; Elton John (who appeared with Kiki Dee and Wham); Paul McCartney; and The Band of the Coldstream Guards, who opened the show by playing 'God Save the Queen' (not the Sex Pistols version!).

6 The 'Don't Die of Ignorance' campaign alerted people to the dangers of HIV/AIDS, which had first been observed in 1981. By 1990, it was estimated that 8 to 10 million people were living with the disease worldwide.

7 Halley's Comet passed across the sky, which occurs every 75 years or so. Unfortunately, it chose to come when the weather in the UK wasn't that good. Many 50-year-olds now, however, may just be the right age to also see its next return in 2061.

8 Chernobyl was the city abandoned in April 1986 following the world's worst nuclear accident. One unexpected result is that, in the absence of human life, the area has since seen a surge in its populations of roe deer, elk, wild boar and wolves. So perhaps nuclear disaster might be good for the environment after all!

YOU KNOW YOU'RE 50 WHEN...

YOU THINK THE BEST ELECTRONIC AND VIDEO GAMES WERE THE FIRST ONES

As a 50-year-old you've lived through the entire history of computer games and watched them develop into an extraordinary, immersive art form. And yet, the things that really get your pulse racing are still the sound of a monophonic synthesizer tune and the pixellated graphics of your youth. But which old video games and their main protagonists can you name?

1   The video table tennis game launched by Atari in 1972.

2   The 1978 sci-fi arcade game which inspired early house music and gave its name to injuries to the elbow and wrist injuries experienced by players.

3   The 1979 arcade game released about 10 years after the event it portrayed actually happened.

4   The arcade game first seen in 1980 in which the protagonist has to eat as many dots as possible while being pursued by four ghosts called Blinky, Pinky, Inky and Clyde.

5   The video-game gorilla who made his first appearance in 1981.

6   The game starring the breakout star from the gorilla game, who was originally known as 'Jumpman'.

7. The 1981 arcade game in which an amphibian has to make its way across a busy road.

8. The 1984 game of Soviet origin involving a deluge of geometrical shapes.

9. The 1984 shooting game involving wildfowl and a laughing dog.

10. The bestselling game console issued in 1989 during its parent company's hundredth anniversary.

YOU KNOW YOU'RE 50 WHEN...

YOU THINK THE BEST ELECTRONIC AND VIDEO GAMES WERE THE FIRST ONES

— ANSWERS —

1 The Atari tennis game was *Pong*, one of the world's first-ever video games. Shifting a dot from one side of a TV screen to the other was so mesmerising that no one noticed that *Pong* was not a very attractive name.

2 *Space Invaders* – many players were diagnosed as suffering from *Space Invaders* wrist or *Space Invaders* elbow. What hope would we have in the event of a genuine alien invasion?

3 *Lunar Lander* – but did Neil Armstrong have to keep feeding 10p pieces into a slot when attempting to land his lunar module on the Moon for real?

4 *Pac-Man* was the Japanese-created arcade game in which a round object has to gobble its way through everything in sight while trying to get away from the four ghosts. Japanese ghost stories became slightly more sophisticated after this.

5 *Donkey Kong*, which sounded more like a terrifying story about a monstrous creature laying waste to Blackpool Pleasure Beach.

6 *Super Mario*. Obviously the people at Nintendo thought the most exciting hero for a video game would be a moustachioed Italian plumber wearing dungarees!

7 *Frogger* – another game played by millions around the world, in which the object is to herd frogs through heavy traffic, something which no one in their right mind had ever attempted to do in real life.

8 *Tetris*. The game was so mesmerising it was obviously the basis of a Soviet plot to overthrow the West by getting everyone hooked on this addictive challenge.

9 *Duck Hunt*, a game in which players had to endlessly shoot ducks, which would come in handy in the event of Planet Earth ever being invaded by waterfowl.

10 Nintendo Game Boy. The Game Boy was an enormous success for Nintendo in 1989, their centenary year. The company had started out producing playing cards, which is probably just as well. Any video consoles released in 1889 would have been rubbish.

YOU KNOW YOU'RE 50 WHEN...

YOU STILL THINK THE FASHIONS OF THE 1970s AND 1980s LOOK STYLISH

Time can be very cruel. It can be particularly cruel if you're 50 and your formative years were spent in the 1970s and 1980s. The styles popular back then will therefore have imprinted themselves so deeply on your memory that you probably still think they look pretty good – despite all the evidence to the contrary! Nevertheless, let's take a wander through your wardrobe and other fashion styles of the 1970s and 1980s.

1   Loons and elephant bells were two types of what?

2   Designer Michael Fish originated which fishy-sounding 1970s men's fashion item?

3   A shag and a wedge were fashions in what?

4   Which couple ran the King's Road boutique called 'Let It Rock', which later morphed into 'Too Fast To Live, Too Young To Die' and then 'Sex'?

5   Which two Native American tribes lent their names to an iconic punk hairstyle?

6   Lycra (or spandex) was launched in 1978. Spandex is an anagram of what appropriately descriptive verb?

7   Which 1980s dress was famously designed by David and Elizabeth Emanuel?

8 What slogan was written on George Michael and Andrew Ridgeley's T-shirts when they performed 'Wake Me Up Before You Go Go' on *Top of the Pops* in May 1984? And which other 1980s band copied the slogan style soon after?

9 A must-have sportswear item of the 1980s took its name from a nineteenth-century circus performer. What was his name?

10 Shoulder pads were much on display in the 1980s TV series *Dynasty*. But what were the names of the shoulder-padded characters played by Joan Collins and Linda Evans?

YOU KNOW YOU'RE 50 WHEN...

YOU STILL THINK THE FASHIONS OF THE 1970s AND 1980s LOOK STYLISH

— ANSWERS —

1. Flared or bell-bottomed trousers, garments specifically designed to make it look like you had your legs on upside down, which is why the widest bits were nearest the ground.

2. The kipper tie. Designer Michael Fish also created dresses for men. Confusingly, the BBC weather forecaster also called Michael Fish was famous for sporting a kipper tie, although he never appeared on screen in a dress.

3 They were two types of hairstyles – going into a hairdresser's and loudly demanding either could lead to unexpected and unfortunate consequences.

4 Malcolm McLaren and Vivienne Westwood. It was in the 'Sex' shop that the Sex Pistols were formed (the original four members were customers and one of them had a Saturday job there). Warning – if you see a 'Sex Shop' today, it probably isn't selling fashionable Vivienne Westwood attire.

5 Mohawk or Mohican. In fact, the hairstyle referred to was more commonly associated with the Iroquois but maybe hairdressers found that too difficult to spell when advertising the style in their windows.

6 Expands, which is what your Spandex clothes may do if you don't go to the gym often enough!

7 Princess Diana's wedding dress – it was one of the great fashion items of the 1980s, but for some reason people didn't start adopting it as everyday wear.

8 The T-shirts designed by Katherine Hamnett for Wham! had the slogan 'Choose Life'. Soon after, similar-looking T-shirts appeared promoting

Liverpool band Frankie Goes to Hollywood, with slogans like 'Frankie Say Relax', 'Frankie Say Arm The Unemployed' and 'Frankie Say What Do You Mean, Pay Royalties to Katherine Hamnett?'

9   Jules Léotard, a famous French trapeze artist who inspired the song 'The Daring Young Man on the Flying Trapeze'. His friends included Pierre Sweatband and Henri Leg-Warmer!

10   Alexis Colby and Krystle Carrington (or were their shoulders genuinely that big?).

YOU KNOW YOU'RE 50 WHEN...

YOU THINK THE CLASSIC ERA FOR MUSIC WAS THE 1980s

If you've ever found yourself arguing that the musical contributions of Elvis Presley, The Beatles and Led Zeppelin were nothing compared to those of Shakin' Stevens or the Goombay Dance Band, this may suggest that you have an unwavering love for the music you grew up with in the 1980s. In which case, you should have no trouble answering the following.

1. Which two records kept Ultravox's 'Vienna' off the top of the charts in February 1981?

2. Which British pop band took their name from a character in the Jane Fonda film *Barbarella*?

3. What was Spandau Ballet's only UK number one hit?

4. Which band had members with the surnames Hay, Craig, Moss and O'Dowd?

5. Which 1982 album is said to have sold over 66 million copies?

6. Which 1982 hip hop single contains the lines: 'It's like a jungle sometimes, It makes me wonder how I keep from goin' under'?

7. Which Manchester band insisted on playing live on *Top of the Pops* on 31 March 1983 and what effect did this have on sales of their hit single?

8. What was the only sound contributed by the musicians in the Frankie Goes to Hollywood single 'Relax'?

9. Which 1987 hit was given a new lease of life via the internet prank known as 'rickrolling'?

10. Which 1989 Madonna video helped lose the singer her sponsorship deal with Pepsi?

YOU KNOW YOU'RE 50 WHEN...

YOU THINK THE CLASSIC ERA FOR MUSIC WAS THE 1980s

— ANSWERS —

1. 'Woman' by John Lennon (which Ultravox must have thought was understandable at the time) and then 'Shaddap You Face' by Joe Dolce Music Theatre (by which time Ultravox must have started to think the record-buying public might be taking the mickey).

2. Duran Duran. The character in *Barbarella*, actually called Durand Durand, was the inventor of the 'positronic ray', which was capable of threatening Earth. So we probably got off lightly with Duran Duran's musical output.

3 'True' – sadly, Spandau Ballet did not think to name the record's B-side 'False'.

4 Culture Club. Lead singer Boy George (O'Dowd) caused some confusion in the 1980s and even managed to come second in an NME poll for both the best-dressed male and best-dressed female of 1983.

5 *Thriller* by Michael Jackson. If you thought the record was thrilling, imagine what it was like getting the royalty cheques!

6 'The Message' by Grandmaster Flash and the Furious Five. In fact, Grandmaster Flash may have been the furious one, as he didn't get to appear on any of the hip hop legends' studio recordings as the result of a dispute.

7 New Order. After they insisted that they should play their single 'Blue Monday' live on *Top of the Pops*, the record dropped down the charts the following week.

8 According to producer Trevor Horn, the only sound they contributed was when they all jumped into a swimming pool together!

9   'Never Gonna Give You Up' by Rick Astley. Supposedly, 39 million prank plays of the song on YouTube up to August 2010 generated a mere $12 share to Rick in royalties. Which suggested a whole new level to the rickrolling prank!

10   'Like A Prayer' – the video seemed to involve a lot of sexy making out with a religious statue in a church. How could anyone find that controversial?

YOU KNOW YOU'RE 50 WHEN...

YOU USE DECADES-OLD TV AND FILM CATCHPHRASES IN DAILY CONVERSATION

Do others look more and more perplexed every time you mention a classic TV or film catchphrase? Is that because they are somehow intellectually deficient? Or is it because your favourite catchphrases are from American films and TV shows from many years before they were born? Which US 1970s, 1980s and 1990s productions and characters were associated with the following catchphrases?

1. 'Whatchu talkin' 'bout, Willis?'

2. 'You wouldn't like me when I'm angry.'

3. 'Just one more thing.'

4. 'I'm going to make him an offer he can't refuse.'

5. 'Hasta la vista, baby.'

6. 'Nanu, Nanu.'

7. 'Who loves ya, baby?'

8. 'Book 'em, Danno.'

9. 'Goodnight, John-Boy.'

10. 'I pity the fool.'

YOU KNOW YOU'RE 50 WHEN...

YOU USE DECADES-OLD TV AND FILM CATCHPHRASES IN DAILY CONVERSATION

— ANSWERS —

1 Gary Coleman as Arnold Jackson in *Diff'rent Strokes*. The 1978 to 1986 sitcom about African American brothers Arnold and Willis Jackson and their life after they move in with white New York businessman Philip Drummond and his daughter Kimberly. Sadly, life turned out to be less fun for the cast after the show ended.

2 David Banner, in the late 1970s TV series *The Incredible Hulk*, which starred Bill Bixby as David Banner and bodybuilder Lou Ferrigno as the Hulk. Ferrigno got less of a clothing allowance on the series than Bixby, but considerably more of a budget for green body paint.

3 Peter Falk as Columbo in the eponymous detective series. If Columbo ever said 'Just one more thing' to a character on the show, you knew it was going to be something they didn't want to talk about.

4 Marlon Brando as Don Corleone in *The Godfather*. With the amount of padding Brando had to stuff into his gob to play the part, it should really have been an offer no one was able to understand!

5 Arnold Schwarzenegger as The Terminator in *Terminator 2: Judgment Day*. In fact, the first person to say this phrase in the 1991 film was the 10-year-old John Connor, as he teaches it to Arnie, along with 'no problemo' and 'eat me'!

6 *Mork and Mindy*. Star of the show Robin Williams was friends at drama school with Christopher Reeve. In the same year that *Mork and Mindy* appeared, Reeve also found fame playing an alien from outer space who makes his home on Earth – Superman.

7 *Kojak*, the bald, lollipop-sucking detective played by Telly Savalas. Once the series hit the screens, Kojak became the epithet of choice for anyone at school who made the mistake of having an overly short haircut.

8 *Hawaii Five-0*: Steve McGarrett would regularly bring episodes to a conclusion by instructing his sergeant Danny Williams to 'book 'em, Danno'. Episodes ending 'Let 'em off with a caution, Danno' tend to be less well remembered.

9 *The Waltons*, the story of a family struggling through the Great Depression in Virginia. There were so many children in the Walton family, saying goodnight to them seemed to take up most of each week's episode.

10 It is often reported that this was said by Mr. T in his role as B. A. Baracus in *The A-Team*. In fact, it was said by Mr. T as boxer Clubber Lang in *Rocky III*. And you can pity any fool who thinks otherwise!

YOU KNOW YOU'RE 50 WHEN...

YOUR FAVOURITE COMEDY SHOWS ARE ALL FROM THE 1980s AND 1990s

You may never have laughed so much as you did in your youth and early adulthood. Well, it was the 1980s and 1990s and there were some very odd fashions around at the time. But it was also a time of classic TV comedy shows. In which of them would you have found the following characters?

1. A talking gorilla, a mime called Alternative Car Park, John McEnroe having his breakfast and a man who is arrested for having curly black hair and thick lips.

2. Sid Snot, Cupid Stunt, Gizzard Puke and Marcel Wave.

3. Del Boy, Rodney, Trigger, Boycie, Raquel and Cassandra.

4. Miss Babs, Berta, Mrs Overall, a waitress who has great trouble carrying soup, and a woman suffering pubic dandruff.

5. A people's poet, a hippie, a punk medical student and a cool person.

6. Mrs Thatcher in a suit, the Queen Mother with a Yorkshire accent, a grey John Major eating peas and Ronald Reagan's missing brain.

7   Edina, Patsy, Saffron and Bubble.

8   Kevin the teenager, Mr Cholmondley-Warner, Tim Nice-But-Dim and Wayne and Waynetta Slob.

9   Arthur Atkinson, Dave Angel Eco Warrior, Bob Fleming, Swiss Toni, Ted and Ralph, a pair of gents tailors and Channel 9.

10 Jarvis, People of Restricted Seriousness and History Today.

YOU KNOW YOU'RE 50 WHEN...

YOUR FAVOURITE COMEDY SHOWS ARE ALL FROM THE 1980s AND 1990s

— ANSWERS —

1. *Not the Nine O'Clock News*, the legendary show featuring Rowan Atkinson, Pamela Stephenson, Mel Smith and Griff Rhys Jones. The memory of the show now 'kinda lingers'.

2. *The Kenny Everett Video Show*, co-written by Kenny, Barry Cryer and Michael McIntyre's dad Ray Cameron.

3. *Only Fools and Horses*, the work of the great John Sullivan, a former BBC scene shifter who made the break into writing when he handed a script to Ronnie Barker.

4   *Victoria Wood as Seen on TV*. Victoria Wood
    emerged from talent show *New Faces* and
    performing funny songs while apparently
    dressed in a tent on *That's Life* to become one
    of the UK's greatest and most-loved comedians
    and writers.

5   *The Young Ones*, the brilliantly anarchic
    comedy starring Rik Mayall, Ade Edmondson,
    Nigel Planer and Christopher Ryan, plus Alexei
    Sayle as the entire Balowski family.

6   *Spitting Image*, the scathingly satirical show
    featuring puppets designed by Peter Fluck
    and Roger Law. Voices were supplied over the
    years by the likes of Harry Enfield, Chris Barrie,
    Steve Coogan, Alistair McGowan, Hugh Dennis,
    Kate Robbins and, of course, Steve Nallon as
    Mrs Thatcher.

7   *Absolutely Fabulous*, which was inspired by a
    French and Saunders sketch. Jennifer Saunders'
    character, Edina Monsoon, took her name
    from real-life husband Ade Edmondson's Eddie
    Monsoon character in the *Comic Strip Presents*
    programmes. Eddie Monsoon had clearly been
    taken in turn from Ade Edmondson's own name.

8 *Harry Enfield's Television Programme*, an endless source of great characters and catchphrases which became slightly less great the more people at work kept repeating them to you.

9 *The Fast Show* – even faster and even more characters from Enfield associates Paul Whitehouse and Charlie Higson and friends.

10 *Newman and Baddiel In Pieces.* Rob Newman and David Baddiel proved comedy was the new rock and roll with this follow-up to *The Mary Whitehouse Experience*. And after finishing the series and playing Wembley Arena, they split up acrimoniously in true rock and roll fashion.

YOU KNOW YOU'RE 50 WHEN…

YOUR SPORTING HEROES ALL RETIRED ABOUT 20 YEARS AGO

In the 1980s and 1990s the world of sport was one of screaming brats, political boycotts, alleged drug cheats and unlikely competitors. Presumably there must have been some sport going on as well. See if the following questions jog your memory.

1. Why did the USA win no medals at the 1980 Olympics?

2. In June 1981, who famously howled 'You cannot be serious!'?

3 In which city did Torvill and Dean achieve a perfect score for their ice dancing at the 1984 Winter Olympics? And which piece of music did they perform to?

4 In 1984, Daley Thompson won the gold medal in the decathlon at the Los Angeles Games. But which events does the decathlon involve?

5 Which boxer took just 91 seconds to knock out which other boxer in Atlantic City, New Jersey on 27 June 1988?

6 Which athlete was stripped of his gold medal in the 100 metres at the 1988 Seoul Olympics?

7 Which team at the 1988 Winter Olympics in Calgary inspired the film *Cool Runnings*?

8   At the same Olympics, which competitor flew like an eagle to come last in both ski jumping events?

9   Which players missed their kicks in the penalty shoot-out that settled the 1990 World Cup semi-final between England and West Germany?

10   Which athlete won the London Marathon six times in the ten years from 1992?

YOU KNOW YOU'RE 50 WHEN...

YOUR SPORTING HEROES ALL RETIRED ABOUT 20 YEARS AGO

— ANSWERS —

1. The USA boycotted the Moscow Games because of the presence of Soviet troops in Afghanistan. A threat that Moscow may have heard as: 'If you don't withdraw your troops, we'll make it much easier for you to win loads of medals!'

2. John McEnroe, in his first-round match against Tom Gullikson at Wimbledon, yelled 'You cannot be serious!' while questioning a line call. This became his catchphrase, provided the title of his autobiography (*Serious*) and is the phrase people have shouted at him in the street ever since.

3 The 1984 Winter Olympics were held in Sarajevo, where Torvill and Dean performed their free dance to a version of Ravel's *Bolero*, albeit greatly condensed from its original 17-minute recording. This was partly to comply with Olympic rules and partly to avoid carving a hole in the ice as the result of 17 minutes skating in circles.

4 100 metres; long jump; shot put; high jump; 400 metres; 110 metres hurdles; discus; pole vault; javelin; and 1500 metres. The only tougher Olympic event is, of course, the Ant-and-Decathlon, in which you have to do all of the above and then eat a kangaroo's testicle.

5 Mike Tyson defeated Michael Spinks. If you'd popped out to make a cup of tea when the fight started, it would have all been over by the time you got back.

6 Canadian sprinter Ben Johnson, following discovery of steroid use, was stripped not only of his Olympic medal but of his 100-metre world record from the year before.

7 The Jamaican bobsleigh team – proof that everyone loves an underdog. No films have so far been made about the bobsleigh winners that year.

8 Eddie 'the Eagle' Edwards, a great British sporting hero who really did fly like an eagle. Well, perhaps one that had just begun flying lessons.

9 Stuart Pearce and Chris Waddle – people probably don't like to remind them about this too often, though.

10 Tanni Grey-Thompson, who also won 16 Paralympic medals and became a member of the House of Lords for good measure.

YOU KNOW YOU'RE 50 WHEN...

YOU THINK THE EVENTS OF THE 1990s HAPPENED EARLIER TODAY

By the 1990s you were an adult, at least theoretically, and were taking the events of the world a bit more seriously. Well, you might have done if you hadn't been out enjoying yourself every night. So did any of the following news stories reach you through the haze of debauchery you were enjoying at the time?

1. Which fast-food restaurant opened for the first time in Moscow on 31 January 1990?

2. Who completed a long walk to freedom when he emerged from Victor Verster Prison on 11 February 1990?

3. Why was Margaret Thatcher seen in tears on 28 November 1990?

4. Who was chased in a white Ford Bronco by the LA Police Department on 17 June 1994?

5. Which Russian president failed to get off a plane at Shannon Airport on 30 September 1994 to meet the Irish leader Albert Reynolds?

6. Which two destinations first appeared on the departure board at London Waterloo Station on 14 November 1994?

7   Derivatives trader Nick Leeson was
    arrested in Frankfurt on 2 March 1995.
    What had he done?

8   What was the connection between
    Tony Blair's election victory in 1997 and
    scientist and TV presenter Professor
    Brian Cox?

9   Which three people were killed in a car
    accident in the Pont de l'Alma tunnel in
    Paris on 31 July 1997? And who was the
    one occupant of the car who survived?

10 On 26 January 1998, who claimed he
    did not have sexual relations with
    which woman?

YOU KNOW YOU'RE 50 WHEN...

YOU THINK THE EVENTS OF THE 1990s HAPPENED EARLIER TODAY

— ANSWERS —

1. McDonalds. After 40 years of cold war, espionage and nuclear threats, the Americans decided that a simpler way to get to the heart of Russia would be to open a fast-food restaurant.

2. Nelson Mandela. After 27 years in prison, the ANC leader walked free, became President of South Africa and won the 1993 Nobel Peace Prize. But it was meeting the Spice Girls in 1997 that he claimed as one of the greatest moments of his life. Well, he had been locked away for a very long time!

3 Mrs Thatcher was seen shedding a tear as she left Downing Street after standing down as Prime Minister and Leader of the Conservative Party. She was sitting in the back seat of a car at the time and, according to some, continued to try to influence the subsequent John Major government as a back-seat driver for some years afterwards.

4 O. J. Simpson. O.J.'s close friend and defence attorney, who sat alongside him throughout the trial, was Robert Kardashian. Whatever happened to his family?

5 Boris Yeltsin failed to get off the plane. Some said he was incapacitated by drink, but his daughter said he had suffered one of his several heart attacks.

6 The Eurostar destinations of Paris Gare du Nord and Brussels-South. The Brussels route passed close to the site of the Battle of Waterloo, while the destination of Waterloo appeared as a potentially unwelcome reminder on the departure board in Paris.

7 Leeson was the rogue trader who brought down Barings, the UK's longest-trading merchant bank. He left the bank with debts of £827 million and a note saying 'I'm sorry'.

8 New Labour's campaign theme for the 1997 election was 'Things Can Only Get Better' by the band D:Ream, whose keyboard player was future Professor Brian Cox. In fact, Brian may not have played on the record itself, but things certainly got better for him afterwards.

9 Diana, Princess of Wales, Dodi Fayed and their driver Henri Paul were all killed in the crash. Diana's bodyguard Trevor Rees-Jones survived, although it is believed that he, like the other passengers, was not wearing a seatbelt.

10 President Bill Clinton claimed he did not have sexual relations with White House intern Monica Lewinsky. Unfortunately for him, she possessed laundry that proved he had!

YOU KNOW YOU'RE 50 WHEN...

YOUR HEAD IS STILL FULL OF THE TV ADVERTS THAT WERE ON IN YOUR YOUNGER DAYS

While walking around the supermarket trying to decide what to have for dinner, do you sometimes hear the products on the shelves singing to you? And, if so, are they singing jolly advertising jingles which were last broadcast on TV in or around the 1980s? If so, you should have no trouble answering the following.

1. In 1980, which product were we told to sprinkle over our carpets to 'put the freshness back'?

2. In 1982, which ice cream was advertised to the tune of 'O Sole Mio'?

3. In 1983, who used a copy of Yellow Pages in his attempts to track down a copy of a book called *Fly Fishing*? And who was the author of the book?

4. Also in 1983, which product was advertised to the tune of 'Que Sera Sera' with the lyrics 'Will it be chips or jacket spuds? Will it be salad or frozen peas? Will it be mushrooms? Fried onion rings? We'll have to wait and see!'

5. In 1985, which beer refreshed the parts that other beers cannot reach?

6. A 1985 advert featured male model Nick Kamen stripping off in a 1950s-style launderette. Which product was being advertised? And which classic tune accompanied the ad?

7   And, according to another advert which sent up the same scenario, how could you tell Nick Kamen didn't drink Carling Black Label?

8   In an advert for BT in December 1987, Maureen Lipman as Beattie (get it?) calls her grandson Anthony to congratulate him on his exam results. Which exams had he passed?

9   In 1989, which product was advertised by Gregor Fisher's 'Baldy Man' character, depicted experiencing a series of problems in a photo booth?

10   Which 1991 advert featured an orange man slapping someone on the cheeks?

YOU KNOW YOU'RE 50 WHEN...

YOUR HEAD IS STILL FULL OF THE TV ADVERTS THAT WERE ON IN YOUR YOUNGER DAYS

— ANSWERS —

1 Shake n' Vac – in the 1980s, they invented a form of talcum powder specially designed for carpets. Even more bizarrely, they managed to persuade us all to buy it.

2 Wall's Cornetto. 'Just one Cornetto, give it to me. Delicious ice cream from Eetalee.' Many thought at the time that the words of all Italian arias must be referring to different types of ice cream!

3 An elderly gentleman called J. R. Hartley was searching for the book *Fly Fishing*, which was

written by J. R. Hartley. The advert was so successful that a book called *Fly Fishing* by J. R. Hartley was created and genuinely published. It must have taken them ages to find someone called J. R. Hartley to write it for them!

4 The advert was actually for Bird's Eye Steakhouse Grills, although you can't help wondering if its chorus of 'Hope it's chips, it's chips! We ho-o-ope it's chips, it's chips!' just encouraged everyone to make themselves some chips!

5 Heineken was the beer that refreshed the parts that other beers cannot reach, although these parts were never specifically mentioned or indicated on an anatomical diagram.

6 To the accompaniment of 'I Heard It Through The Grapevine', Nick Kamen stripped off his Levi 501s and T-shirt. This gained him the admiration of various women in the laundrette, even though his behaviour clearly indicated that he was unable to afford more than one change of clothing.

7 In a Carling Black Label advert, comedians Mark Arden and Steve Frost pointed out that a Kamen lookalike hadn't washed his underpants. By contrast, they were sitting in the laundrette completely starkers.

8 Anthony claimed he had failed almost everything
– Maths, English, Physics, Geography, German,
Woodwork and Art – but he had managed to
pass Pottery and Sociology, causing his gran to
exclaim, 'You get an 'ology, you're a scientist!'

9 Hamlet cigars. The Baldy Man spent some
time adjusting his single strand of comb-over
hair before his seat plummeted just as the
photo booth flashed to take his picture. The ad
was clearly making the subliminal point that
smoking is very bad for you and may cause
significant hair loss.

10 Tango. Adverts for the fizzy drink featured
a bizarre, fat, orange man attacking and/
or kissing people in the street at unexpected
moments. But could it be the same round,
orange man who was subsequently elected
President of the United States?

YOU KNOW YOU'RE 50 WHEN...

YOUR FAVOURITE FILMS ARE ALL FROM THE 1980s AND 1990s

By the 1980s you were able to get in to see films that were above U certification. You might even have started paying for your tickets with your own hard-earned cash rather than with a fiver from mum and dad. And perhaps you settled down in the darkened cinema next to your boyfriend or girlfriend – or, failing that, maybe a large carton of popcorn. But which films from those impressionable years of the 1980s and 1990s featured the following characters?

1. Lieutenant Pete 'Maverick' Mitchell, Charlotte 'Charlie' Blackwood, Lieutenant Tom 'Iceman' Kazansky and Lieutenant Nick 'Goose' Bradshaw (1986)

2. Ellen Ripley, Corporal Dwayne Hicks, Carter J. Burke and Newt Jorden (1986)

3. Dan Gallagher, Beth Rogerson Gallagher, Ellen Gallagher and Alex Forrest (1987)

4. Harry Burns, Sally Albright, Marie Fisher and Jess Fisher (1989)

5. T-800 (Model 101), T-1000, John Connor and Sarah Connor (1991)

6. Mr White, Mr Orange, Mr Blonde, Mr Blue, Mr Brown, Mr Pink, 'Nice Guy' Eddie and Joe Cabot (1992)

7   Phil Connors, Rita Hanson, Larry the cameraman and Ned Ryerson (1993)

8   Dr Alan Grant, Dr Ellie Sattler, Dr Ian Malcolm, John Hammond, Dennis Nedry, Robert Muldoon, Ray Arnold and Tim and Lex Murphy (1993)

YOU KNOW YOU'RE 50 WHEN...

YOUR FAVOURITE FILMS ARE ALL FROM THE 1980s AND 1990s

— ANSWERS —

1. *Top Gun*, the film which gave us 'Take My Breath Away' by Berlin and which featured a then 24-year-old Tom Cruise, which seems to be the age he has remained ever since!

2. *Aliens*, the follow-up to 1979's *Alien*, which means that the next sequel should have been titled *Alienses*?

3. *Fatal Attraction*, a story of adultery, sexual obsession and vengeance, but mainly we remember the poor rabbit and the origin of the phrase 'bunny boiler'!

4 *When Harry Met Sally.* Spoiler alert – Harry does indeed meet Sally in this movie!

5 *Terminator 2: Judgment Day.* You can tell it's a sci-fi classic, because the list of characters sounds like the index of a technical catalogue.

6 *Reservoir Dogs.* Despite the title, no dogs were in fact hurt during the course of this film, although just about everyone else involved was!

7 *Groundhog Day.* Ironically, a film that these days seems to get repeated on TV every single day!

8 *Jurassic Park.* OK, the cast also involved a Tyrannosaurus rex and several raptors, but that would have made the question a little too easy.

YOU KNOW YOU'RE 50 WHEN...

THE MOST RECENT POP MUSIC YOU LIKE IS FROM THE 1990s

In the 1990s, you may have been a wide-eyed raver going mad for it while Britpop ruled, Blur battled it out with Oasis and a series of records went to the top of the charts and seemed to sit there for the rest of the year. Have a go at the following to see if you're still sorted for Es and quiz!

1 In 1991, which record achieved the longest-ever unbroken run at number one in the UK singles chart?

2 Which 1992 single achieved the longest run at number one in the UK singles chart for a female artist?

3 In 1994, which record achieved the second-longest unbroken run at number one in the UK singles chart?

4 And which Euro disco hit finally knocked the answer to number 3 off the top spot?

5 Which singles were involved in the legendary battle between Blur and Oasis in the summer of 1995?

6 Which song by ageing Spanish crooners Los del Río became a worldwide hit in 1996 and a favourite at wedding receptions ever since?

7 Which Britpop star invaded the stage during Michael Jackson's performance at the 1996 BRIT Awards?

8 In which order did the Spice Girls sing their solo lines on their first single 'Wannabe' in 1996?

9 Which 1997 single by the band Aqua was the centre of a legal case between MCA Records and toy manufacturer Mattel?

10 Which Labour politician had a bucket of ice water poured over him by 'Tubthumping' hit makers Chumbawamba at the 1998 BRIT Awards?

YOU KNOW YOU'RE 50 WHEN...

THE MOST RECENT POP MUSIC YOU LIKE IS FROM THE 1990s
— ANSWERS —

1   Bryan Adams was number one for 16 weeks from July to October 1991 with '(Everything I Do) I Do It For You' – a chart record for him, an endurance record for the rest of us!

2   'I Will Always Love You' by Whitney Houston, an absolute belter which should never be attempted by a non-professional. It is the only single to have been number one for ten weeks in the USA, UK and Australian charts.

3   Wet Wet Wet were number one with 'Love Is All Around' for 15 weeks from May until September 1994. Legend has it that the band then decided to delete the record from sale. Even they had heard it enough by then!

4 'Saturday Night' by Whigfield, a number one hit across Europe. So that's millions of people who have had that tune stuck in their heads at least one night a week ever since.

5 'Country House' by Blur and 'Roll With It' by Oasis. Blur won this battle of the bands, because their record went to number one and kept Oasis at number two. However, the number of extra disks put out with different versions of 'Country House' may have meant that Oasis made more of a profit out of their record.

6 Los del Río's song was 'Macarena'. They had formed in 1962, which meant there had been a 34-year lead-up to the song and associated dance being launched onto the world. This means they are due to have another massive hit in 2030.

7 Thinking that Michael Jackson was presenting himself a bit too much like Jesus during his performance of 'Earth Song', Pulp singer Jarvis Cocker hopped up and joined Jacko's dancers on stage, waggling his bum at the King of Pop and at the audience. Following this collaboration, Jarvis and Jacko did not go on to work together on any further musical projects.

8 The Spice Girls stepped up to the solo microphone in the following order: Mel B, Geri, Mel C and Emma. Victoria, meanwhile, danced around in the background waiting to get a solo line, which, unfortunately, never came on this particular tune.

9 The lyrics of 'Barbie Girl' by Aqua referenced both Barbie and her boyfriend Ken. The record went to number one across Europe and in the USA, but the manufacturers of the Barbie doll were seemingly displeased by this extensive free publicity.

10 John Prescott, the Labour Deputy Prime Minister, had icy water poured over him by Chumbawamba vocalist Danbert Nobacon (aka Nigel Hunter), possibly because New Labour had refused to support the Liverpool dockworkers' strike, or possibly because Danbert Nobacon was incensed by the sight of a man who had clearly enjoyed quite a lot of bacon!

YOU KNOW YOU'RE 50 WHEN...

YOU HEARD THE FOLLOWING GREAT QUOTES WHEN THEY HAD JUST BEEN UTTERED

As a 50-year-old, you've lived through memorable times. But see if you can answer the following about some legendary words spoken by the great and the good during your lifetime.

1   According to former Labour Chancellor of the Exchequer Denis Healey, being attacked by which politician was 'like being savaged by a dead sheep'? (1978)

2   Who said, 'No one would remember the Good Samaritan if he'd only had good intentions; he had money as well'? (1980)

3   Which member of the Royal Family warned British students visiting China, 'If you stay here much longer, you'll all be slitty-eyed'? (1986)

4   Which 1989 film memorably featured the line, 'I'll have what she's having!'?

5   Who described what as an *annus horribilis*? (1992)

6   Who claimed he had experimented with 'marijuana a time or two and I didn't like it. I didn't inhale...' (1992)

7   In 2000, who explained an unexpected victory with the words 'They misunderestimated me'?

8 About whom did Tony Blair say 'John is John' during the 2001 general election campaign? And what had John recently done to prompt this slightly exasperated explanation?

9 Who said: 'There are known knowns; there are things we know we know. We also know there are known unknowns; that is to say we know there are some things we do not know. But there are also unknown unknowns...'? (2002)

10 Which of the Spice Girls proudly claimed, 'I haven't read a book in my life'? (2005)

YOU KNOW YOU'RE 50 WHEN...

YOU HEARD THE FOLLOWING GREAT QUOTES WHEN THEY HAD JUST BEEN UTTERED

— ANSWERS —

1 Healey was referring to future Conservative Chancellor and Deputy Prime Minister Geoffrey Howe. Dead sheep or not, it was Howe's resignation speech in November 1990 which helped bring down Mrs Thatcher.

2 Mrs Thatcher reminded us that the true meaning of one of Jesus' most famous and religiously moving parables was the importance of being filthy rich.

3 It was of course Prince Philip, making one of his many contributions to international relations.

4 *When Harry Met Sally*. The line was uttered by director Rob Reiner's mum, Estelle, after Sally's fake-orgasm scene. The restaurant featured in the scene still offers customers the chance to sit where Sally did.

5 The Queen described her experiences in 1992 in these words. This was the year when Prince Charles separated from Princess Diana, Andrew Morton's book about Diana was published and a fire broke out at Windsor Castle. Some, however, thought the reference to *annus horribilis* meant she was confessing to an outbreak of haemorrhoids.

6 Then presidential nominee Bill Clinton claimed that he had picked up a joint when he was a student in England, but it was alright because he hadn't in fact inhaled. This defence has never worked for other drug users when questioned by the authorities.

7 Newly elected US President George W. Bush. Many of us did 'misunderestimate' him – we thought there could never be a worse president! How little did we know back then.

8 The John in question was John Prescott, the then Deputy Prime Minister. Prescott had been campaigning in Rhyl, North Wales when he launched a left hook at a man who had just thrown an egg at him from point-blank range. In Prescott's defence, the man was sporting a particularly annoying mullet.

9 Then US Defence Secretary Donald Rumsfeld rendered the lack of evidence about Iraq's weapons of mass destruction ever so much clearer with these words!

10 Victoria Beckham, aka 'Posh Spice'. This presumably meant that she hadn't even read her own autobiography published four years earlier.

YOU KNOW YOU'RE 50 WHEN...

YOU NEED TO LOOK UP THE ANSWERS TO THE FOLLOWING QUESTIONS ON THE INTERNET

You've reached 50 and that means you've lived to an age where you have ready access via the internet to the answers to the following vital questions about the time you were born. We could have tried including all the possible answers for every 50-year-old reader, but it would have made the book quite big. So, instead, see if you can find the answers to the following yourself.

1   What was the number one record in the charts the week that you were born?

2   What were the main news headlines on the day you entered the world?

3   Who were the Prime Minister, Chancellor of the Exchequer, Home Secretary and Foreign Secretary at the time?

4   What was the weather like on the day you were born?

5   What were the top films at the box office that week?

6   What was on TV that evening?

7   Which celebrities were born on the same day as you?

8   Which famous people died around the time you were born?

9   What was the population of the world at the time?

10   How much did a loaf of bread, a pint of milk and a gallon of petrol cost?

FILL IN YOUR ANSWERS BELOW

1

2

3

4

5

6

7

8

9

10

If you're interested in finding out more about our books, find us on Facebook at **Summersdale Publishers** and follow us on Twitter at @Summersdale.

www.summersdale.com